It's Time to Eat VEGAN CASSEROLE

Walter the Educator

Silent King Books
A WhichHead Entertainment Imprint

Copyright © 2024 by Walter the Educator

All rights reserved. No part of this book may be reproduced in any manner whatsoever without written per- mission except in the case of brief quotations embodied in critical articles and reviews.

First Printing, 2024

Disclaimer

This book is a literary work; the story is not about specific persons, locations, situations, and/or circumstances unless mentioned in a historical context. Any resemblance to real persons, locations, situations, and/or circumstances is coincidental. This book is for entertainment and informational purposes only. The author and publisher offer this information without warranties expressed or implied. No matter the grounds, neither the author nor the publisher will be accountable for any losses, injuries, or other damages caused by the reader's use of this book. The use of this book acknowledges an understanding and acceptance of this disclaimer.

It's Time to Eat VEGAN CASSEROLE is a collectible early learning book by Walter the Educator suitable for all ages belonging to Walter the Educator's Time to Eat Book Series. Collect more books at WaltertheEducator.com

USE THE EXTRA SPACE TO TAKE NOTES AND DOCUMENT YOUR MEMORIES

VEGAN CASSEROLE

It's dinner time, the table is set,

It's Time to Eat Vegan Casserole

The yummiest meal is what we'll get!

Out of the oven, all warm and whole,

It's time to eat vegan casserole!

Packed with veggies, colors so bright,

Sweet potatoes, broccoli, what a sight!

Beans and rice, a savory layer,

Every bite's a little prayer.

Cheesy on top, but vegan, of course,

Made from plants, it's a kind-hearted force.

With every scoop, the flavors blend,

A casserole feast that'll never end.

Peas and carrots, squash, and kale,

This dish is strong, it'll never fail!

A sprinkle of spices, a dash of fun,

The magic of casserole has begun.

It's Time to Eat Vegan Casserole

It's warm and cozy, perfect to share,

A hug on a plate, made with care.

One bite, two bites, oh, so good,

It's all the flavors of the neighborhood!

Serve it with love, and maybe some bread,

A side of salad, or greens instead.

Healthy and tasty, good for all,

Vegan casserole answers the call.

The earth says thank you, the animals too,

For eating plants, a kind thing to do.

With every forkful, you're making it right,

Caring for the world with every bite.

Gather your family, gather your friends,

The joy of casserole never ends.

Sitting together, sharing a meal,

It's Time to Eat

Vegan Casserole

Casserole's warmth is the love you feel.

When the dish is empty, don't despair,

We can make another with love to spare.

Cooking is fun, it makes us whole,

Let's celebrate vegan casserole!

So grab your plate, it's time to eat,

A vegan casserole can't be beat!

Layer by layer, the flavors shine,

It's Time to Eat

Vegan Casserole

This dinner's amazing, yours and mine!

ABOUT THE CREATOR

Walter the Educator is one of the pseudonyms for Walter Anderson. Formally educated in Chemistry, Business, and Education, he is an educator, an author, a diverse entrepreneur, and he is the son of a disabled war veteran. "Walter the Educator" shares his time between educating and creating. He holds interests and owns several creative projects that entertain, enlighten, enhance, and educate, hoping to inspire and motivate you. Follow, find new works, and stay up to date with Walter the Educator™ at WaltertheEducator.com

www.ingramcontent.com/pod-product-compliance
Lightning Source LLC
LaVergne TN
LVHW012052070526
838201LV00082B/4050